Welcome to Adventure Club!

This book is all yours,
so add your
fingerprints and glue
in your passport.
Then, get ready. The
fun is about to begin.

**Exploring The Universe Of God's Promises
Junior Activity Book**

Adventure Club
Cook Ministry Resources
a division of Cook Communications Ministries
4050 Lee Vance View
Colorado Springs, CO 80918-7100

Scripture quotations are from the Holy Bible, New International Version (NIV), © 1973, 1978, 1984 by the
International Bible Society. Used by permission of Zondervan Bible Publishers.

ISBN: 0-7814-5224-4

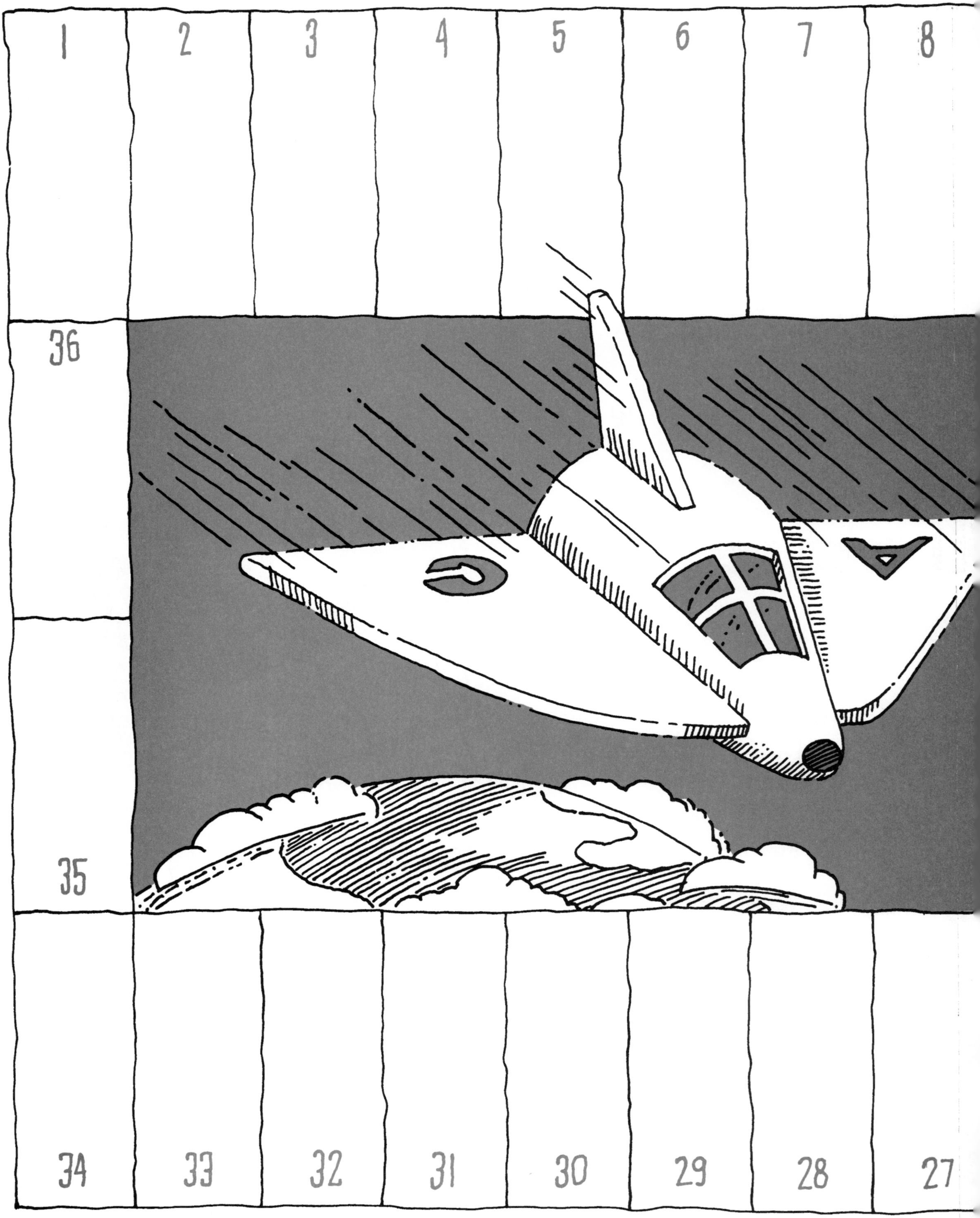
1
2
3
4
5
6
7
8
36
35
34
33
32
31
30
29
28
27

9 10 11 12 13 14 15 16

17

Chart your Course.
Each Club meeting, record your points. Give yourself 1 point for each of the following: attendance, bringing a visitor, memorizing the verse, and completing the activity page.

18

26 25 24 23 22 21 20 19

PRAYER LOG

DATE	MY REQUEST	GOD'S ANSWER	DATE ANSWERED

DATE	MY REQUEST	GOD'S ANSWER	DATE ANSWERED

DATE	MY REQUEST	GOD'S ANSWER	DATE ANSWERED

DATE	MY REQUEST	GOD'S ANSWER	DATE ANSWERED

TEE-RIFIC PARENTS

Design a T-shirt that encourages other kids to treat their parents with love and respect. These words might help you think of an idea: obey, love, help, listen, cooperate, respect, honor.

Now write a letter to a local store, telling them why they should sell your product.

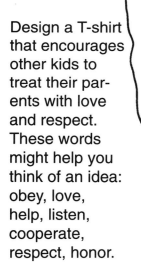

DEAR ...

TO:

Memorize God's Promise: Exodus 20:12
"Honor your father and mother, so that you may live long in the land the Lord your God is giving you."

2.

All About ME

❏ Name three things you like about your mom.

❏ Name three things you like about your dad.

Think It Over

God had a wonderful plan when He made families. He wanted family members to love and honor each other.

Is it easy or difficult for you to honor your parents?

If it is easy for you to honor your parents, why is it easy?

If it is difficult, how can Jesus help you be more able to honor them?

Family Feature

As parents of Adventurers, join your child in this week's lesson by doing the following at home:

❏ Read how Samuel honored his parents in 1 Samuel 3.

❏ Plan a special meal together and have family members tell something special about Mom or Dad.
- A Favorite memory
- A Funny story
- An accomplishment
- An Embarrassing moment

AMAZING WISDOM

King Solomon was a wise man. When he was granted one wish, he chose wisdom over everything else. That was a very wise choice.

As you find your way through this decision-making maze, add each step to the acrostic below:

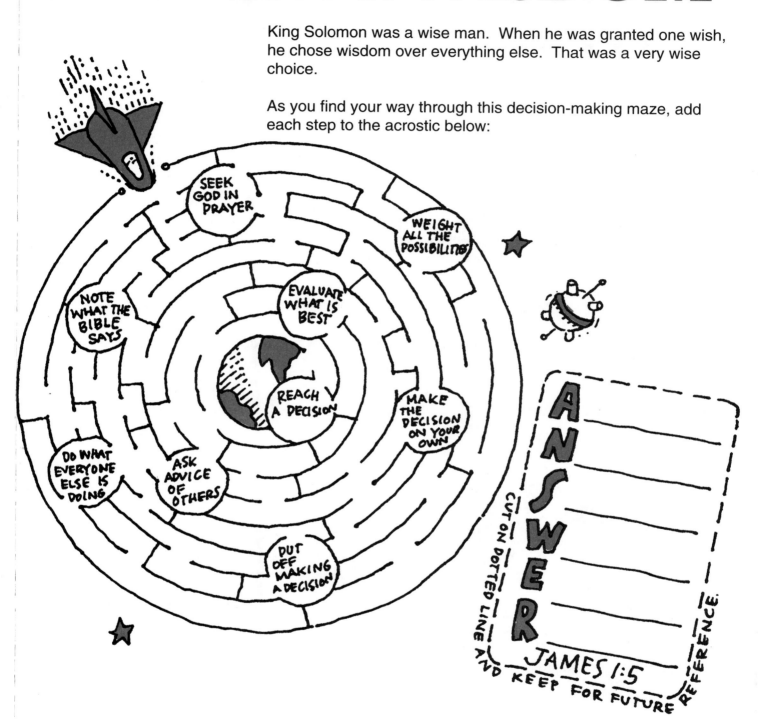

SEEK GOD IN PRAYER

WEIGHT ALL THE POSSIBILITIES

NOTE WHAT THE BIBLE SAYS

EVALUATE WHAT IS BEST

REACH A DECISION

MAKE THE DECISION ON YOUR OWN

DO WHAT EVERYONE ELSE IS DOING

ASK ADVICE OF OTHERS

PUT OFF MAKING A DECISION

ANSWER

JAMES 1:5

CUT ON DOTTED LINE AND KEEP FOR FUTURE REFFERENCE.

Memorize God's Promise: James 1:5
"If any of you lacks wisdom, he should ask God, who gives generously to all without finding fault, and it will be given to him."

7.

All About ME

❏ List or draw three things you wish for the most.

Think It Over

James 1:5 says that God will give you wisdom and help to make good choices.

When you need to make a decision or choice, how will God help you and give you wisdom?

Family Feature

As parents of Adventurers, join your child in this week's lesson by doing the following at home:

Many of Solomon's wise sayings can be found in the Book of Proverbs.

❏ Each day this week discover with your family a word of wisdom for the day.

(M)	• Proverbs 1:8
(T)	• Proverbs 20:20
(W)	• Proverbs 10:19
(Th)	• Proverbs 11:28
(F)	• Proverbs 12:18
(Sat)	• Proverbs 13:16
(Sun)	• Proverbs 16:24

HELP FOR A DYING PLANET

Find out what help is promised in God's Word.
Fill in each square with a letter from the column
directly below it, marking out letters as you use
them. A black square signals the end of a word.
The Word Bank will help you.

Word Bank

AND MAN TO
TO WHAT CAME
OF FOR SAVE
THE LOST
WAS SON SEEK

Memorize God's Promise: Luke 19:10

9.

❏ Name someone who is very special to you.

Why is this person special?

Some of our friendships and relationships aren't very "harmonious." We may be angry with friends or hurt by something they did to us.

What would you do to be at peace with someone you are angry with or was hurt by?

If you feel that your friendship with God isn't very "harmonious," what can you do to be at peace with God?

As parents of Adventurers, join your child in this week's lesson by doing the following at home:

❏ Look at some examples from the Bible of people who were a blessing to others.
  • Abraham gave his nephew first choice of land (Genesis 13)
  • Esther asked the king to save her people (Esther 5)
  • Joseph forgave his brothers (Genesis 45)
  • Zaccheus returned tax money to people (Luke 19:1-10)
  • David spared Saul's life (1 Samuel 26)
  • Jesus forgave those who killed Him (Luke 23:34)

What can your family learn from the lives of these people?

A RESCUE MISSION!

Put one letter in each square. Keep on stacking the words until
you have completed the puzzle. All the words are from the life
of Abraham and Isaac.

Words

Isaac
Abraham
Sarah
ram
Canaan
Moriah
sacrifice
angel
voice
obedience
bush
thicket
trust

Memorize God's Promise: John 3:16
"For God so loved the world that he gave his one and only Son, that
whoever believes in him shall not perish but have eternal life."

10.

All About ME

What would you say is the most important event or thing that has happened in your life?

Think It Over

Jesus died on the cross to take the punishment for sin because He loves you and you are important to Him.

How do you feel knowing that you are important to Jesus and He loves you?

Family Feature

As parents of Adventurers, join your child in this week's lesson by doing the following at home:

❑ Read John 3:16. Put the name of each family member in place of the words, "the world." For example: "For God so loved Lee that he gave his one and only Son."

STARS *of the* FAMILY

Using your Bible, locate the missing members of Jesus' family tree. Luke 3 gives the genealogy of Jesus.

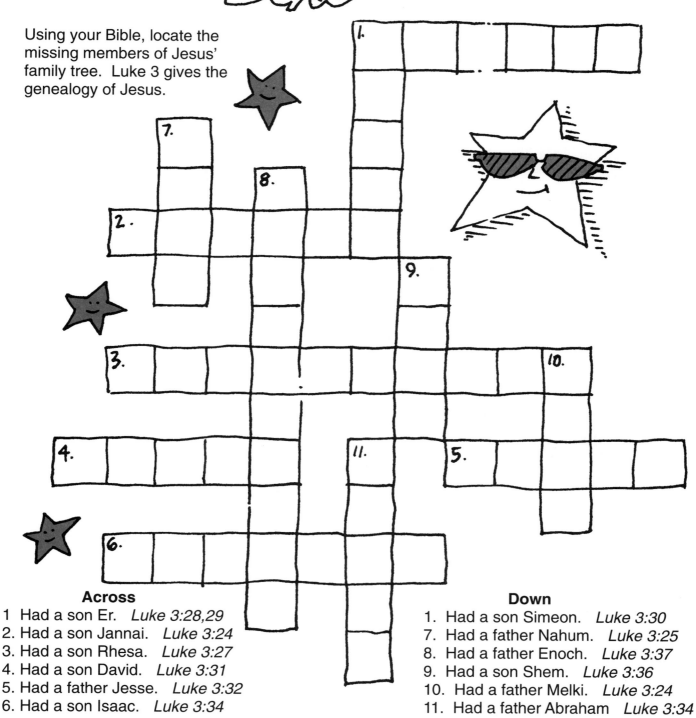

Across

1 Had a son Er. *Luke 3:28,29*
2. Had a son Jannai. *Luke 3:24*
3. Had a son Rhesa. *Luke 3:27*
4. Had a son David. *Luke 3:31*
5. Had a father Jesse. *Luke 3:32*
6. Had a son Isaac. *Luke 3:34*

Down

1. Had a son Simeon. *Luke 3:30*
7. Had a father Nahum. *Luke 3:25*
8. Had a father Enoch. *Luke 3:37*
9. Had a son Shem. *Luke 3:36*
10. Had a father Melki. *Luke 3:24*
11. Had a father Abraham *Luke 3:34*

Memorize God's Promise: Genesis 28:14b and 15a
". . . All peoples of the earth will be blessed through you and your off-spring. . . . I will not leave you until I have done what I have promised you."

❑ Finish this sentence:

My favorite thing to do with my neighborhood friends is

_____.

Do you have family members who are not Christians? Do they know how important Jesus is to you? Name two ways you can show them.

As parents of Adventurers, join your child in this week's lesson by doing the following at home:

❑ Draw your family tree with as many relatives on it as you can. Hang it up and pray for each person on that tree sometime during the week.

KINGDOM BUILDERS

... is _____ , _____ , and _____ . ROMANS 14:17

... is _____ . LUKE 17:21b

... is _____ ... JOHN 18:36

The Bible says God's Kingdom is in this world, but not of it. What does this mean?

Believers (members of the Kingdom) are also called to be in the world but not of it. How can you become a member of God's Kingdom?

Memorize God's Promise: II Samuel 7:16
"Your house and your kingdom will endure forever before me; your throne will be established forever."

What is your favorite time of day?

Jesus is sometimes called the King of Kings.

What do you think this name means?

❏ Make a list of words that would describe the kind of King Jesus is.
   For example:
   • Good
   • Generous

As parents of Adventurers, join your child in this week's lesson by doing the following at home:

❏ Write a "Kingdom Proclamation" stating how your family will follow and obey the King of Kings.

WISDOM *from* HEAVEN

James 1:5 promises that God will always give wisdom to anyone who sincerely seeks it. Read the following verses and use the code to list three sources for advice when we need wise answers to life's questions.

$\overline{U}\ \overline{B}\ \overline{V}\ \overline{H}\ \overline{M}\ \overline{X}\ \overline{W}$
Proverbs 1:8

$\overline{J}\ \overline{V}\ \overline{L}\ \overline{H}\ \overline{M}\ \overline{C}\ \overline{W}$
Proverbs 13:20

$\overline{K}\ \overline{Q}\ \overline{C}$
Proverbs 3:5-6

CODE!

B=A C=D H=E
J=F K=G
M=N Q=O L=I
V=R W=S U=P
X=T

Read Proverbs 13:20 again. Advice that contradicts God's Word is never wise counsel. What does this tell us about who we should choose as friends?

Memorize God's Promise: Isaiah 9:6
"For to us a child is born, to us a son is given, and the government will be on his shoulders. And he will be called Wonderful Counselor, Mighty God, Everlasting Father, Prince of Peace."

Name a friend who is a wise adviser to you. Give an example of his or her wise counsel.

Jesus is called the "Wonderful Counselor." He is able to help with any problem you may have.

Why would Jesus be a good Person to talk to about your problems?

As parents of Adventurers, join your child in this week's lesson by doing the following at home:

❑ Read John 3:1-21. Nicodemus had many questions for Jesus.

If you could ask Jesus any question, what would it be?

❑ Decorate a shoe box and label it "Question Box." Encourage family members to put in questions. Allow family time each week to discover answers together.

JESUS: THE BRIGHTEST STAR

List names for Jesus or words which describe Him.

_____
_____
_____
_____
_____
_____
_____
_____
_____
_____
_____

Now use the list above in writing an original poem, song or rap to share with other small groups.

Memorize God's Promise: Isaiah 9:6
"For to us a child is born, to us a son is given, and the government will be on his shoulders. And he will be called Wonderful Counselor, Mighty God, Everlasting Father, Prince of Peace."

14.

All About ME

What is your name?

Do you know why your name was chosen?

Do you know what your name means?

Think It Over

Jesus is called "Mighty God." This name tells us that Jesus is powerful and He is God.

How is Jesus different from any other person who ever lived or ever will live?

Family Feature

As parents of Adventurers, join your child in this week's lesson by doing the following at home:

❑ Have every family member give a "gift" of a Bible verse to other family members. Write the verses on pieces of paper, wrap them up, and exchange gifts. (For encouraging Bible verses, check out the Psalms!)

Decode the message using the key.

Three ways I can show compassion:

1. _____

2. _____

3. _____

KEY:

A=1   G=7   M=13   S=19
B=2   H=8   N=14   T=20   Y=25
C=3   I=9   O=15   U=21   Z=26
D=4   J=10   P=16   V=22
E=5   K=11   Q=17   W=23
F=6   L=12   R=18   X=24

Memorize God's Promise: Isaiah 9:6
"For to us a child is born, to us a son is given, and the government will be on his shoulders. And he will be called Wonderful Counselor, Mighty God, Everlasting Father, Prince of Peace."

15.

What is your favorite holiday? Why?

❏ Think of a time when someone showed compassion to you.

How did you feel?

What sometimes keeps you from showing compassion to others?

As parents of Adventurers, join your child in this week's lesson by doing the following at home:

❏ Search the Bible to find how family members can show compassion.
- Romans 12:16-18
- Galatians 5:22, 23
- Galatians 6:1, 2
- Ephesians 4:31, 32
- Colossians 3:12-15
- I Peter 3:8-9

WHAT'S IN A NAME

How many names do you have? You probably have a first, last and middle name. You may also have a nickname and several title names, like son, daughter, cousin, brother or sister. These names tell something about you.

Jesus also has many names. Using your Bible, find the names listed in the references below and write each one on a name tag.

Scriptures: John 14:6, John 3:2, John 6:48, John 10:11, Matthew 21:5, John 8:12, Matthew 8:19, Isaiah 9:6a

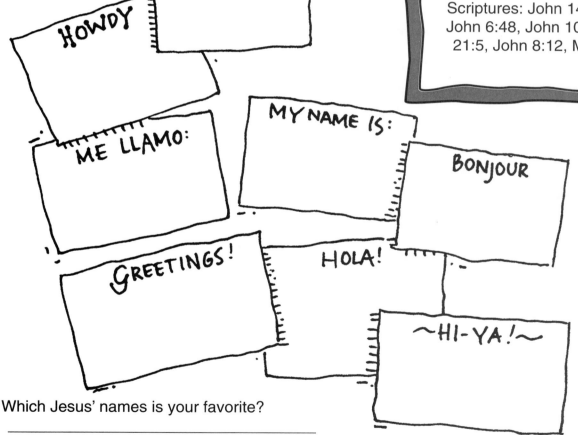

HELLO!

HOWDY

ME LLAMO:

MY NAME IS:

BONJOUR

GREETINGS!

HOLA!

~HI-YA!~

Which Jesus' names is your favorite?

_____

Why? _____

_____

Memorize God's Promise: Isaiah 9:6
"For to us a child is born, to us a son is given, and the government will be on his shoulders. And he will be called Wonderful Counselor, Mighty God, Everlasting Father, Prince of Peace."

16.

❏ Tell about a time when you were a peacemaker.

Jesus is called the "Prince of Peace."

What does this name tell you about Him?

What areas of your life aren't very "peaceful" now? How can Jesus help?

As parents of Adventurers, join your child in this week's lesson by doing the following at home:

❏ Read Romans 12:14-21.

❏ Make a list of ways to be a peacemaker.

How can you be a peacemaker at home?

GLOBAL GUILT

God has a way out of sin and guilty feelings. Decode the Bible verse by finding the place on the chart where the shape and number columns intersect. The first word is done for you.

What words express that your sins are forgiven:

1. _____

2. _____

3. _____

Memorize God's Promise: I John 1:9

22.

What was the best thing that happened to you this week?

Often when we've done something wrong we are afraid to admit it because we fear people won't like us. When we admit our sin to God, however, He continues to love us and care about us.

What might keep you from admitting your sin to God and asking for forgiveness?

As parents of Adventurers, join your child in this week's lesson by doing the following at home:

❏ Read Psalm 51.

❏ Make a list of all the things God does for us when we confess our sins.

❏ Thank God for His everlasting love.

NO GROUCHES

Read each statement and decide whether it is "TRUE" or "FALSE." Circle the letter under your choice and then write the letters in order in the blank below. The word will tell you about a behavior that is not pleasing to the Lord.

	TRUE	FALSE
1. God told Jonah to go to Tarshish.	D	M
2. Jonah went to Ninevah right away.	I	O
3. God caused a great wind upon the sea.	O	M
4. When they threw Jonah overboard the winds and the storm stopped.	D	S
5. The Bible tells us that a whale swallowed Jonah.	T	I
6. Jonah gave up once inside the fish and blamed God for his troubles.	H	N
7. After Jonah prayed to the Lord, the fish spit him up on to dry land.	E	R
8. This time Jonah went to Ninevah as the Lord had directed.	S	B
9. The people of Ninevah did not repent and Jonah was happy to see them get what they deserved.	B	S

We can do better than _____

Name two things you can do to turn a bad mood around. Share strategies with your small group.

TURN THIS FROWN UPSIDE DOWN

23.

Memorize God's Promise: Psalm 42:5
"Why are you downcast, O my soul?. . . Put your hope in God."

What was your worst day this week?

How do you feel when things don't go your way?

When you feel sad, angry, irritable, or frustrated because things didn't go as you had wanted, it helps to remember that God is in charge and can help.

❏ If you're feeling upset because something hasn't gone your way, take some time to pray and tell God how you feel. Ask Him to help you.

As parents of Adventurers, join your child in this week's lesson by doing the following at home:

❏ Work as a family to develop five positive steps you can take to make your family atmosphere more joyful and less tense.

1.

2.

3.

4.

5.

HEAVENLY DELIVERANCE

Read Acts 12:1-19 and unscramble the words below, taken from this story of God's deliverance of Peter:

hancis   _ _ O_O_
rugsad   O _ _ _ _ _
lecl   _O_ O

Now, unscramble the circled letters to name Peter's deliverer: _ _ _ _ _

The Bible is full of stories of angels protecting God's people and sending messages to them on earth. List three things you learned about angels from this account in Acts 12.

1._____

2._____

3._____

Memorize God's Promise: Psalm 91:11
"For he will command his angels concerning you to guard you in all your ways."

29.

All About ME

❏ Describe a time you felt afraid.

Think It Over

Would you agree or disagree with this statement, "Only things I can see are real"?

❏ Make a list of things you can't see, yet you know are real.

How would you describe angels to someone who didn't think they really existed?

Family Feature

As parents of Adventurers, join your child in this week's lesson by doing the following at home:

❏ Read the story of Peter's escape from prison in Acts 12:1-19.

❏ Look up these Bible verses to learn more about angels:
- Psalm 103:20
- Luke 1:26-33
- Matthew 1:20
- Daniel 6:19-22
- Luke 2:8-12
- Matthew 18:10

RE-ENTRY TO EARTH

In the box below, each letter stands for the letter that comes after it in the alphabet. (A=B; B=C; C=D; Z=A) Decode the passage and you will find a verse that tells about Jesus' return.

SGHR   RZLD   IDRTR   VGN   GZR   ADDM

SZJOM   EQNL   XNT   HMSN   GDZUDM'   VHKK

BNLD   AZBJ   HM   SGD   RZLD   VZX   XNT

GZUD   RDDM   GHL   FN   HMSN   GDZUDM

Write another verse telling about the second coming in code; then, have a friend decipher it. (Hint: Look in your concordance under the words "come," "descend," "thief," and "moment" to find a verse about Christ's return)

30.

Memorize God's Promise: Acts 1:11

All About ME

What is the biggest surprise you've ever had?

Think It Over

Have you ever eagerly awaited the visit of someone special? Who was it?

How did you feel as you waited for this special person to come?

❑ Tell how Jesus' return will be different than any other visit by someone special.

Family Feature

As parents of Adventurers, join your child in this week's lesson by doing the following at home:

❑ Read about Jesus' promise to return in I Thessalonians 4:13-18.

❑ Have each family member complete this sentence:
   "When I think about the promise of Jesus' return to earth I feel _____."

GOOD NEWS POSTAL SERVICE

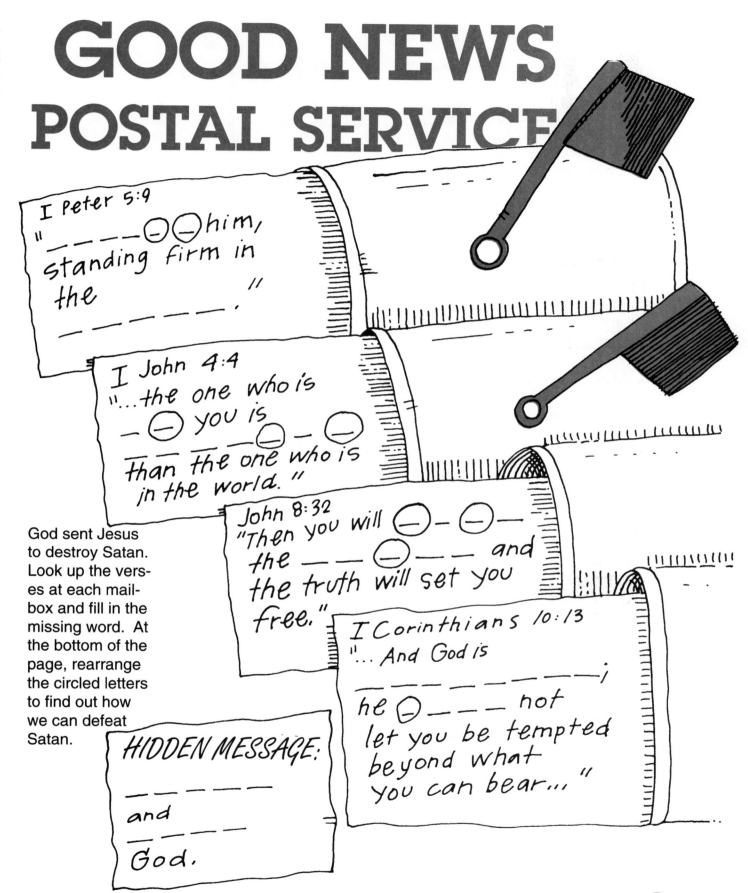

I Peter 5:9
"_ _ _ _ ⊖⊖ him, standing firm in the _ _ _ _ _."

I John 4:4
"...the one who is _ ⊖ you is _ _ _ _ ⊖ _ _ _ than the one who is in the world."

John 8:32
"Then you will ⊙ _ ⊙ _ the _ _ ⊙ _ _ and the truth will set you free."

I Corinthians 10:13
"...And God is _ _ _ _ _ _ _ _; he ⊖ _ _ _ not let you be tempted beyond what you can bear..."

God sent Jesus to destroy Satan. Look up the verses at each mailbox and fill in the missing word. At the bottom of the page, rearrange the circled letters to find out how we can defeat Satan.

HIDDEN MESSAGE:
_ _ _ _ _ _
and
_ _ _ _
God.

Memorize God's Promise: James 4:7
"Submit yourselves, then, to God. Resist the devil, and he will flee from you."

31.

What is one thing you like to do best with your family?

Often times things that are evil are made to look exciting and fun.

❏ Make a list of things you see on TV, in movies, in stores, or anywhere else that show evil things or behavior as being exciting.

How are these things the opposite of what Jesus teaches?

As parents of Adventurers, join your child in this week's lesson by doing the following at home:

❏ Spend some time evaluating how your family spends time together.

     To have a strong caring family the family members need to spend time together. Satan knows that and sometimes he will tempt family members to stay busy and separate from the family.

❏ Plan some regular family times together to strengthen the support and bonds in your family.

❏ Read the following Bible verses and talk about how they apply in your family:
        • James 4:7
        • I Peter 5:8, 9

BE A WINNER

Work your way through the maze to victory with Jesus! But make sure you make the right decisions!

READ YOUR BIBLE

SWEARING AT SCHOOL

FIGHTING WITH OTHERS

VICTORY!

GO TO CHURCH

CHOOSE GOOD FRIENDS

STEALING FROM YOUR PARENTS

FIGHT THE DEVIL

Memorize God's Promise: I Corinthians 15:57
"But thanks be to God! He gives us the victory through our Lord Jesus Christ."

32.

What is your favorite family vacation memory?

When Satan is destroyed, God will be the winner.

❏ Name a person you know who is a winner. How can you be a winner in God's eyes?

As parents of Adventurers, join your child in this week's lesson by doing the following at home:

❏ Read Revelation 20:7-10

How can your family choose to follow God?

❏ Make a commitment to resist the devil and then tell each family member about it in one week.

NEW BODIES

Design a poster that tells people they will get new bodies in heaven. (Ideas: people not getting tired or sick, disabled people getting out of wheelchairs, etc.) Be creative!

(LITTLE DIPPER)

Memorize God's Promise: Philippians 3:20, 21
"But our citizenship is in heaven. And we eagerly await a Savior from there, the Lord Jesus Christ, who, by the power that enables him to bring everything under his control, will transform our lowly bodies so that they will be like his glorious body."

33.

Who would you most like to look like?

The new body that God will give us when we live in heaven with Him will be exactly what we will need.

What are some things you hope you'll be able to do in heaven?

As parents of Adventurers, join your child in this week's lesson by doing the following at home:

❏ Plant a small garden of flowers or vegetables. Use pots or a garden plot in your yard.

The new plants are alive and beautiful.

❏ Read Philippians 3:20.

Our glorious bodies will be alive and beautiful.

CITY IN THE STARS

You have been chosen by the Children's Video Network to create a TV commercial for the New Jerusalem-a city where there will be no darkness, sickness, death, pain, nor sorrow. How would you "sell" someone on heaven? On the TV screens below, draw your televised pictures and write narration for the commercial.

MONITOR 1

MONITOR 2

MONITOR 3

Memorize God's Promise: John 14:2
"In my Father's house there are many rooms. . . I am going there to prepare a place for you."

34.

What is the most unusual experience you have ever had?

Jesus understands the sad feelings that we have. He wants us to come to Him for comfort and help when we are sad.

What is something that makes you sad?

How can Jesus help and comfort you?

What do you think it will be like to live someplace where there is no sadness?

As parents of Adventurers, join your child in this week's lesson by doing the following at home:

❑ Think about different relatives and what is happening in their lives.

❑ Spend some time praying for relatives and family members.

HEAVEN BOUND

If you have trusted Jesus as your Savior, you can be assured an eternity in heaven. Use the verses listed to complete the "Heavenly Citizenship Guarantee" below.

Heavenly Citizenship Guarantee

I. _____ in God's son guarantees _____ life with God. (John 3:16)

II. Believers will be given eternal bodies as _____ of heaven. (Phil. 3:20-21)

III. No ONE can snatch the believer from God's ____. (John 10:28) Signed, God.

If you have not trusted Jesus as your Savior, consider these promises from Scripture. Ask a Christian parent, teacher or friend to pray for your understanding of the abundant life God offers. (John 10:10)

Memorize God's Promise: I Corinthians 15:54b
"Death has been swallowed up in victory."

35.

What do you think the world will be like 10 years from now?

God created us and wants us to enjoy our life on Earth. Sometimes people feel afraid or sad about dying because they don't want to leave their life on Earth.

What are three things you really enjoy doing?

What are three things that will be really special about living with Jesus after your life on earth is over?

As parents of Adventurers, join your child in this week's lesson by doing the following at home:

❑ Read these Bible verses about death and living forever.
- I Corinthians 15:3-11
- I Corinthians 15:12-22
- I Corinthians 15:45-57

❑ Share together as a family about what happens when we die.

RAINBOW of PROMISES

Listed below are a few of God's promises. Match each promise with the correct Bible verse.

Promise	**Verse**
eternal life	I John 1:7
forgiveness	I John 5:11,12
wisdom	Philippians 3:20, 21
power	Romans 2:11
loves everyone	James 1:5
joy	Nehemiah 8:10
protection	Isaiah 40:31
renewed strength	Acts 1:8
fellowship	Psalm 91:11
new bodies	Matthew 6:14

Put a star by your favorite verse and then share with your Basket Talk small group why you like it.

36.

Memorize God's Promise: Psalm 145:13b
"The Lord is faithful to all his promises and loving toward all he has made."

If you could change one thing in your life, what would it be?

Psalm 145:13 says, "The Lord is faithful to all his promises and loving toward all he has made."

Have you ever had someone break a promise to you? How did you feel?

Our memory verse says that the Lord is faithful to all His promises. What does that mean?

God gives us promises because He loves us and wants to give us assurance and hope. He will never break His promises!

As parents of Adventurers, join your child in this week's lesson by doing the following at home:

❏ Make a list of God's promises. Write them on shelf paper or some other roll of paper and see how long your list can be.

What is your family's favorite promise?

AUTOGRAPHS